Lindsay Choudhry has taught children in schools in the UK and US for over 20 years. She has worked with school leaders in developing approaches to literacy, advising on provision for pupils with learning challenges and with UNICEF on the Rights Respecting School Award.

Lindsay enjoys many volunteer roles including teaching chess club in school and managing a girls' cricket team. She lives in Surrey, England, in a house full of Lego and books, with her husband, two beautiful children and two mischievous bunnies.

HUMBLE BEE

LINDSAY CHOUDHRY

AUSTIN MACAULEY PUBLISHERS™

LONDON ★ CAMBRIDGE ★ NEW YORK ★ SHARJAH

A CIP catalogue record for this title is available from the British Library.

ISBN 9781398465350 (Paperback)
ISBN 9781398465367 (Hardback)
ISBN 9781398465374 (ePub e-book)

www.austinmacauley.com

First Published 2023
Austin Macauley Publishers Ltd®
1 Canada Square
Canary Wharf
London
E14 5AA

For my bee-autiful, bee-loved family.

For Arabella and Maximus, the best story makers in the world!

To Moorad for bee-lieving in this little story.

And to Mum and Dad.

Honey Bee watched, with curiosity
As out of the log came a large, fluffy bee.
"Hmmm, black and yellow... yet not like me?"
She wondered out loud,
"What bee could it be?"

Honey Bee asked, but the bee didn't reply
She was busy seeking pollen in a flower nearby,
Bee hovered, and wobbled as she landed on a tree,
Honey Bee called out,
"Are you a STUMBLE BEE?"

Bee shook her head as she landed on a leaf,
Her legs a little shaky, she soon tumbled underneath.
Wings buzzing fast, she flew amazingly,
Honey Bee asked,
"Are you a TUMBLE BEE?"

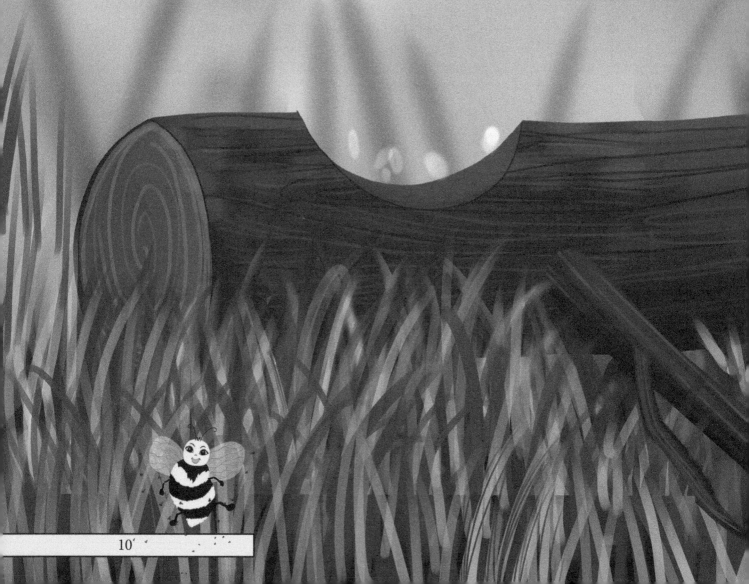

Bee was getting stronger, much braver too,
She flew right across the garden, there was so much
work to do!
Collecting lots of pollen, some dropping carelessly,
Honey Bee had an idea...
"Are you a FUMBLE BEE?"

Bee worked harder now, this pollen was for the queen!
She was keen to do a good job, but her fumbling
had been seen.
Flying back towards her nest once more, Bee
grumbled noisily,
Honey Bee enquired,
"Are you... A GRUMBLE BEE?"

Bee smiled, she blushed, and she quietly murmured,
But with wings buzzing furiously, her words could
not be heard.
Honey Bee tried one more guess, she asked dramatically,
"Could it be, are you, perhaps... a MUMBLE BEE?"

"No, I'm a Bumble Bee, of course, collecting pollen for the queen,
It's not like making honey, my work is rarely seen."
"Oh no," said Honey Bee. "It's not just the queen you feed,
Have you stopped to see what happens while you're spreading all this seed?"

It was Bee's turn to be curious, she listened with intent,
As Honey Bee told the story of how flowers spread
their scent.
"When you fly out of your busy nest, where is it that
you go?
You fly straight towards those flowers, don't you wonder
how you know?

They display their brightly coloured petals, share their
dazzling smell,
Keeping lots of pollen inside, delicious nectar as well.
As you sip this sugary drink, the pollen sticks to
your hairs,
You're having such a fabulous time; this all
happens unawares!

On and on you fly, visiting all the flowers,
Rubbing pollen over each one... Bee, you have
magical powers!
These flowers can make more and more because you
share their seeds,
Without you, Bee, there would be no flowers,
only weeds!

Flowers, trees, vegetables, fruit, they grow in just
one place,
They cannot reach their friends, to share a
warm embrace.
So Bee, you do that for them, as well as feed the queen.
Now can you see how clever you have been?"

Bee smiled. She beamed! She'd never felt so proud,
How wonderful it was to hear that story told out loud.
"BUMBLE BEE might be your name, but I'll tell you
what I see...
Without you, this world wouldn't be the same, you are...

HUMBLE BEE."

Did you know ...

All of these delicious, healthy plants are pollinated by bees! If you have eaten any of these crops, you might like to thank the humble bee for helping it to grow.

Almonds	Gooseberries
Apples	Grapes
Asparagus	Horseradish
Aubergine	Kale
Beans	Lettuce
Beetroot	Mustard
Blackberries	Onions
Brussel Sprouts	Parsley
Cabbage	Peaches
Cantaloupe Melon	Pears
Cauliflower	Plums
Celery	Pumpkins
Cherries	Radishes
Chestnuts	Raspberries
Chives	Rhubarb
Clover	Squashes
Cranberries	Strawberries
Cucumber	Sunflowers
Currants	Sweet potatoes
Garlic	Turnips
	Watermelon

It is believed that bees pollinate nearly 80% of all our food crops... no wonder we call them 'Busy Bees'!

How to invite the humble bee into your garden...

Try planting some of the bees' favourite flowers and plants.
Bees have excellent colour vision, so the brighter your garden
with flowers, the quicker the bees will find it.
The plants with healthy nectar will keep them busy and very
happy indeed.

Bergamot
Chives
Crocus
Echinacea
Foxglove
Lavender
Liatris
Lupine
Marigold
Mint
Nasturtium
Pansies
Peonies
Snap Dragon
Sunflowers
Thyme